Follow that Star

A Christmas Musical for Key Stage 2

Susie Hare

kevin mayhew

kevin mayhew

First published in Great Britain in 2000 by Kevin Mayhew Ltd
Buxhall, Stowmarket, Suffolk IP14 3BW
Tel: +44 (0) 1449 737978 Fax: +44 (0) 1449 737834
E-mail: info@kevinmayhewltd.com

www.kevinmayhew.com

8 7 6 5 4 3 2 1

ISBN 978 1 84003 600 8
ISMN M 57024 738 3
Catalogue No. 1450189

Cover design: Rob Mortonson
Music setting: Rob Danter
Text setting: Margaret Lambeth

Printed and bound in Great Britain

A note about copyright in musicals

Copyright has existed for hundreds of years as a means of protecting the worth of a piece of music or text. It provides income for the composer and publisher and helps to keep the works available in print at an affordable price.

Performance Licence

Any public performance of a piece of copyright music requires a licence. Music remains protected by copyright for 70 years after the death of the composer.

Even if you do not intend to charge an entrance fee for your performance, it is necessary to apply for a licence and the minimum fee will still be payable. If you are staging more than one performance without an admission charge, you need only pay the minimum licence fee once.

If you are charging for admission, the Performance Licence will cost 10% of gross ticket sales, plus VAT, subject to the minimum fee (see page 48).

The only time a performing fee is not payable is when the musical is performed within a worship service and forms part of the act of worship.

Photocopying Licence

The words and music of the songs in our musicals are protected by copyright and may not be photocopied without permission. The music may not be photocopied at all – users are expected to purchase enough copies for those performers who require the full music. The texts may be copied for learning purposes only, provided that:

> The following acknowledgement is included on each copy:
> **© Kevin Mayhew Ltd. Used by permission from** *(name of musical).*
> **Licence number** XXXX XXXX XXXX.
>
> You pay a copyright fee of £10.00 (inc. VAT), which should be added to your performance licence cheque (payable to Kevin Mayhew Ltd).
>
> All copies are destroyed after use.

Please note that music and texts of our musicals are not covered by a CCL licence.

Duplicating CDs

Unfortunately we are unable to give permission for copying the accompanying CDs. It is illegal to duplicate any copyright sound recording, even for home use.

If you have any queries about copyright in Kevin Mayhew publications, please call our Copyright Department on 01449 737978.

There is a photocopiable licence application form at the back of our musicals.

This work is dedicated to the choir of Alton Convent, by whom it was first performed under the direction of Celia Hayes.

Contents

1	In the days of Emperor Augustus	*Full choir*	6
2	No room	*Full choir*	12
3	Do not be afraid	*Solo angel – Angel choir – Full choir*	16
4	Shepherd rock	*Full choir*	20
5	Who am I?	*Solo shepherd – Full choir*	26
6	Herod was having a bad day	*Full choir – Wise men – Herod*	31
7	King of the Jews	*Full choir*	35
8	Follow that star	*Wise men – Full choir*	35
9	Do not be afraid (reprise)	*Solo angel – Angel choir – Full choir*	44

Main Characters

Narrator – Star

Soloists – Shepherd
Herod
Wise men
Angel

Approximate Duration – 30 minutes

FOLLOW THAT STAR

Text and music: Susie Hare

In the days of Emperor Augustus

In the days of Emperor Augustus,
throughout all of Rome there was a census.
Ev'ry one must go, each his name to show
on the register of his home town.

1 If the Emperor decreed it
all the people had to heed it,
ev'ry person in the Empire had to obey.
Had to go to the officials,
give their name and their initials,
had to keep the lineage from going astray.
People ev'rywhere, bustling here and there,
ev'ry one in Rome going back home.

Refrain

2 Censuses were so they knew
just what was what and who was who,
there was an awful lot to do in councils that night.
All the details of descendants
and the names of all dependants;
throughout all of Rome they had to get it just right.
People ev'rywhere, bustling here and there,
ev'ry one in Rome going back home.

Refrain

All the streets were packed with people,
all the inns were going to be full,
ev'rywhere was hustle, bustle, oh what a sight!
All the landlords busy raking
in the money they were making,
suddenly they'd upped their profits just in one night!
People ev'rywhere, bustling here and there,
ev'ry one in Rome going back home.

1. In the days of Emperor Augustus

15
mf
1. If the Em - per - or de - creed it all the peo - ple had to heed it,
2. Cen - sus - es were so they knew just what was what and who was who, there
mf
17
ev - 'ry per - son in the Em - pire had to o - bey.
was an aw - ful lot to do in coun - cils that night.
19
Had to go to the off - i - cials, give their name and their in - i - tials,
All the de - tails of de - scend - ants and the names of all de - pend - ants;
21
had to keep the li - ne - age from go - ing a - stray.
through - out all of Rome they had to get it just right.
Peo - ple ev - 'ry - where,

24
bust-ling here and there, ev - 'ry one in Rome go-ing back home.
28
1.
2.
In the days of Em-per-or Au -
31
gus - tus through-out all of Rome there was a cen - sus.
34
Ev - 'ry one must go, each his name to show on the re - gis - ter

37
of his home town.
40
All the streets were packed with peo - ple, all the inns were going to be full,
All the land-lords bu - sy ra - king in the mo - ney they were ma - king,
42
ev - 'ry - where was hus - tle, bus - tle, oh what a sight!
sud - den - ly they'd upped their pro - fits just in one night!
44
Peo - ple ev - 'ry-where, bus- tling here and there, ev - 'ry one in Rome go-ing back

Narrator Packed in like sardines they were – people all over the place. From where I was, I could see everything that was happening very clearly. You can take it from me – it was Bethlehem bedlam!

I'm the star of the show, by the way – heavenly body variety. I'm the big, bright one that everyone talks about, so I guess you may have heard of me. I'm here to give you a sort of star's eye-view of what went on in Bethlehem all those years ago.

It was the time when every one in the Roman Empire had to go back to their home town to be registered in a census. That wasn't exactly the greatest fun for anyone, to be honest; but for one poor man called Joseph, who had to come all the way from Nazareth, it was especially inconvenient. He came with Mary, his wife-to-be and she was just about to give birth. Well, as you can imagine, they were more desperate than most to find somewhere to stay the night.

No room

1 Joseph went down to register with Mary,
from Nazareth to Bethlehem.
Walking beside her donkey on the journey
Joseph was going home again.
So many people to Bethlehem came;
ev'rywhere they tried the answer was the same:

'No room in the inn, there's nothing we can do.
No room in the inn, we have no room for you.
No room in the inn, there's nothing we can do.
No room in the inn, we have no room for you.'

2 They'd had a long and dusty road to travel,
both of them tired and weary now.
Joseph must keep on knocking at each doorway;
they had to find a place somehow.
Then a kind innkeeper, seeing their plight,
offered to them a stable for the night.

'No room in the inn, except a stable bare.
No room in the inn, but you may rest in there.
No room in the inn, except a stable bare.
No room in the inn, but you may rest in there.'

And on that night, whilst all the world was sleeping,
under the star in Bethl'hem town,
a babe was born, whom all the world was seeking;
the love of heav'n, to earth come down.
The love of heav'n, to earth come down.

2. No room

Unhurried
mp
5
mp
1. Jo- seph went down to re - gis - ter with Ma - ry, from Na - za - reth to
2. They'd had a long and dus - ty road to tra - vel, both of them tired and
8
Beth - le - hem. Walk-ing be - side her don - key on the jour - ney
wea - ry now. Jo - seph must keep on knock-ing at each door-way;
11
Jo-seph was go - ing home a - gain. So ma - ny peo - ple to
they had to find a place some-how. Then a kind inn-keep - er,

14
Beth- le- hem came; ev - 'ry- where they tried the an- swer was the
see - ing their plight, off -ered to them a sta - ble for the
17
mf
same: 'No room in the inn, there's no-thing we can do. No
night. 'No room in the inn, ex - cept a sta - ble bare. No
mf
20
1.
2.
room in the inn, we have no room for you. No have no room for
room in the inn, but you may rest in there. No you may rest in
23
you.'
there.'
mp

Slower
And on that night, whilst all the world was sleep-ing, un-der the star in
Beth-l'hem town, a babe was born, whom all the world was seek-ing;
the love of heav'n, to earth come down. The love of
heav'n to earth come down.
rit.

Narrator What a relief for Joseph and Mary when they found somewhere to stay. Perhaps it wasn't quite the cosy little B&B they would have chosen, but given Mary's condition, it was available just in the nick of time.

Not many babies are born in a stable – well, not many babies as special as this one. And this one was *really* special – unique, in fact. You won't find anyone else who was conceived by the Holy Spirit, born of the virgin Mary and made man, I can tell you. They called him Jesus.

Now, as this was an event that was going to change the world, it had to be told somehow. No televisions, telephones, faxes or internets in those days; but there *were* angels and it was angels who first sang out the good news.

Do not be afraid

Solo angel

Do not be afraid of the song I sing.
Do not be afraid of the news I bring.
For today you'll see a baby who will be
the greatest king in history.

Angel choir

Do not be afraid of the song we sing.
Do not be afraid of the news we bring.
For today you'll see a baby who will be
the greatest king in history.

Full choir

Glory to God in the highest heaven.
Glory to God in the highest heaven.
And peace to men on earth,
and peace to men on earth.
And peace to men on earth,
and peace to men on earth.

Repeat

Last time: Glory to God.

3. Do not be afraid

14
song we sing. Do not be a-fraid of the news we bring.
17
For to-day you'll see a ba-by who will be the great-est king in
20
(Full Choir)
ff
his-to-ry. Glo - ry to God in the
ff
23
high - est hea - ven. Glo - ry to

26
God in the high - est heav - ven. And peace to men on
f
f
30
earth, and peace to men on earth. And peace to men on
34
1.
2.
earth and peace to men on earth. peace to men on
38
rit.
ff
earth. Glo - ry to God.
rit.
ff
8

Narrator Now, you might think that God would send his angels to the most *important* people in the land. After all, this was the most important news that the world was ever to hear.

But no! God chose to send them to humble shepherds because he wanted to make a point. He wanted everyone to know that this baby had been sent for *all* kinds of people, important *and* ordinary. So the angels turned up in a field, of all places!

Imagine: you're a lowly shepherd, just doing a spot of sheep counting and all of a sudden the sky is full of angels. 'Do not be afraid', they say. And well they might!

Shepherd rock

1 To tell the truth, those shepherds had
the kind of night that drove them mad;
there wasn't really much to do
and they were feeling bored.
Then all at once the sky went bright
(the only fun they'd had all night)
and when they looked those shepherds saw
an angel of the Lord.

'You gotta leave your flock and do the shepherd rock.
You gotta leave your flock and do the shepherd rock.
Go on rocking down to Bethl'hem town.
There you will find in a humble cattle stall,
one who is born to be Lord of all.
You gotta leave your flock and do the shepherd rock.
You gotta leave your flock and do the shepherd rock.
Go on rocking down to Bethl'hem town.'

2 The light had left them rather dazed,
the news had left them quite amazed;
it wasn't quite the kind of thing
that happened ev'ry day.
So when the angels left the skies,
they all got up and rubbed their eyes
and then the shepherds left their sheep
and hurried on their way.

4. Shepherd rock

17
on - ly fun they'd had all night) and when they looked those shep-herds saw an
all got up and rubbed their eyes and then the shep-herds left their sheep and
21
an - gel of the Lord. 'You got - ta leave your flock and do the
hur- ried on their way.
25
shep-herd rock. You got - ta
28
leave your flock and do the shep-herd rock.

31
Go on rock-ing down to Beth l'hem town.
35
f
There you will find in a hum-ble cat-tle stall,
f
39
one who is born to be Lord of all.
43
p
You got-ta leave your flock and do the shep-herd rock.
p

47
You got - ta leave your flock and do the shep-herd rock.
50
Go on rock - ing
53
D.C.
down to Beth - l'hem town.'
56
Go on rock - ing down to Beth - l'hem town.

Narrator And so the shepherds went rocking, and possibly rolling too, down to Bethlehem to see the baby.

When they went into the stable they were so excited to be there, but at the same time they felt . . . well, they felt almost as if they didn't *deserve* to be there. They were only ordinary shepherds but, as soon as they saw Jesus, they realised that this was no ordinary baby; not because he was lying in a cattle stall, although that did make him rather unusual, but because there was just . . . *something* about him.

It wasn't anything they could have put into words, even if they *had* been good at talking – which they weren't. All they knew was that it was something very special; something very special indeed.

Who am I?

Solo shepherd

1 Who am I that I sould be
here at so special a birth?
Who am I that I should see
Jesus, the King of the earth?
Only a humble shepherd,
nothing at all I bring,
only this song I sing.

2 Who am I that I should be
here in this cattle stall?
Who am I that I should see
Jesus, the Lord of all?
Only a humble shepherd,
nothing at all I bring,
only this song I sing.

Full choir and shepherd

Only a humble shepherd,
nothing at all I bring . . .

Solo shepherd

. . . only this song I sing.

5. Who am I ?

Unhurried
mp
(Solo Shepherd)
mp
1. Who am I that I should be here at so spe - cial a birth? Who am I that I should see Je - sus, the King of the earth?
2. Who am I that I should be here in this cat - tle stall? Who am I that I should see Je - sus, the Lord of all?

20
On - ly a hum - ble shep - herd,
25
no - thing at all I bring, on - ly this
30
song I sing.
35
(Full Choir)
(Hum)

40
45
50
(Full Choir and Shepherd)
On - ly a hum - ble shep - herd,
54
no - thing at all I bring,

Narrator When the shepherds had seen Jesus, they went, as fast as their legs could carry them, to tell all their friends the amazing news. And their friends told *their* friends and so the word was spread.

It so happened that some wise men who lived in the East, had seen me shining in the sky and knew from this that the baby must have been born. They made a long camel-journey to Bethlehem and started asking people where they could find Jesus. When King Herod heard that they were looking for the new-born baby, he got very anxious. He was the king, after all. And he wasn't at all keen to hear there was another that was greater – and just a baby at that!

This baby may have been good news for mankind but he was definitely not good news for Herod!

Herod was having a bad day

Full choir 1

Herod was having a bad day
and Herod was rather upset.
He had a horrible feeling,
that there was worse to come yet.
Herod looked out of his window,
some camels were heading his way;
up to the palace rode wise men
and this is what they had to say:

Wise men

'Please tell us; where is the baby
who's born to be King of the Jews?
We've seen his star in the east
and we thought maybe you had some news.'

Full choir 2

Herod was forced to admit it,
of this he knew nothing at all;
so he assembled together,
the priests and the teachers of law.
Herod felt suddenly threatened,
for this he just couldn't allow.
Pride was his number one problem
but he'd have to swallow it now.

Herod

'Please tell me; where is the baby
who's born to be King of the Jews?
They've seen his star in the east
and they thought maybe we had some news.'

Full choir 3

'He will be born in Judaea,
the town of Bethlehem,
just as the prophet has written,
but what will you say to the men?'
Herod must think of an answer;
he racked all the brains in his head.
Calling the men to a meeting,
he smiled at them and said:

Herod

'There is a baby in Bethlehem,
born to be King of the Jews.
Please let me know when you find him
and then I can worship him too.'

6. Herod was having a bad day

17
up to the pa-lace rode wise men and this is what they had to say:
Pride was his num-ber one prob-lem but he'd have to swal-low it now.
Call-ing the men to a meet-ing, he smiled at them and said:
21
(Wise Men, verse 1
Herod, verses 2, 3.)
'Please tell us;
'Please tell me;
'There is a
25
where is the ba-by who's born to be King of the Jews? We've seen his
where is the ba-by who's born to be King of the Jews? They've seen his
ba-by in Beth-le-hem, born to be King of the Jews. Please let me
29
star in the east and we thought may-be you had some news.'
star in the east and they thought may-be we had some news.'
know when you find him and then I can wor-ship him too.'

Narrator The wise men brought gifts of gold, frankincense and myrrh to give to the baby. You might think this was overdoing it a bit, considering that the shepherds took nothing; but, as I said, both the poor and ordinary and the rich and important came to Jesus then. And nothing's changed since.

With such precious gifts on board, the wise men were naturally anxious to find Jesus. And so, as you would expect, they did a wise thing. They followed me!

King of the Jews

Full choir

He's gonna be the King of the Jews.
He's gonna be the King of the Jews.
OK, maybe he's only a baby,
but he's gonna be big news.
He's gonna be the King of the Jews.
He's gonna be the King of the Jews.
It sounds absurd but you can take our word,
he's gonna be, yeah, you wait and see,
he's gonna be big news.

Repeat

Immediately followed by:

Follow that star

Wise men

We'll go, follow that star,
shining, shining bright.
We'll go, follow that star,
shining in the night.

We'll get on our camels
and, keeping our eyes
fixed on the star in the skies,
we'll ride to the place where it stops
and we'll see, that's where the baby will be.

We'll go, follow that star,
shining, shining bright.
We'll go, follow that star,
shining in the night.

Continued over . . .

Full choir

We'll go, follow that star,
shining, shining bright.
We'll go, follow that star,
shining in the night.

We'll get on our camels
and, keeping our eyes
fixed on the star in the skies,
we'll ride to the place where it stops
and we'll see, that's where the baby will be.

We'll go, follow that star,
shining, shining bright.
We'll go, follow that star,
shining in the night.

Full choir

He's gonna be the King of the Jews.
He's gonna be the King of the Jews.
OK, maybe he's only a baby,
but he's gonna be big news.
He's gonna be the King of the Jews.
He's gonna be the King of the Jews.
It sounds absurd but you can take our word,
he's gonna be, yeah, you wait and see,
he's gonna be big news.

Sung together with:

Wise men

Go, follow that star.
Go, follow that star,
shining, shining bright.
Go, follow that star.
Go, follow that star,
shining in the night.
Follow that star.
Follow that star.

7. King of the Jews

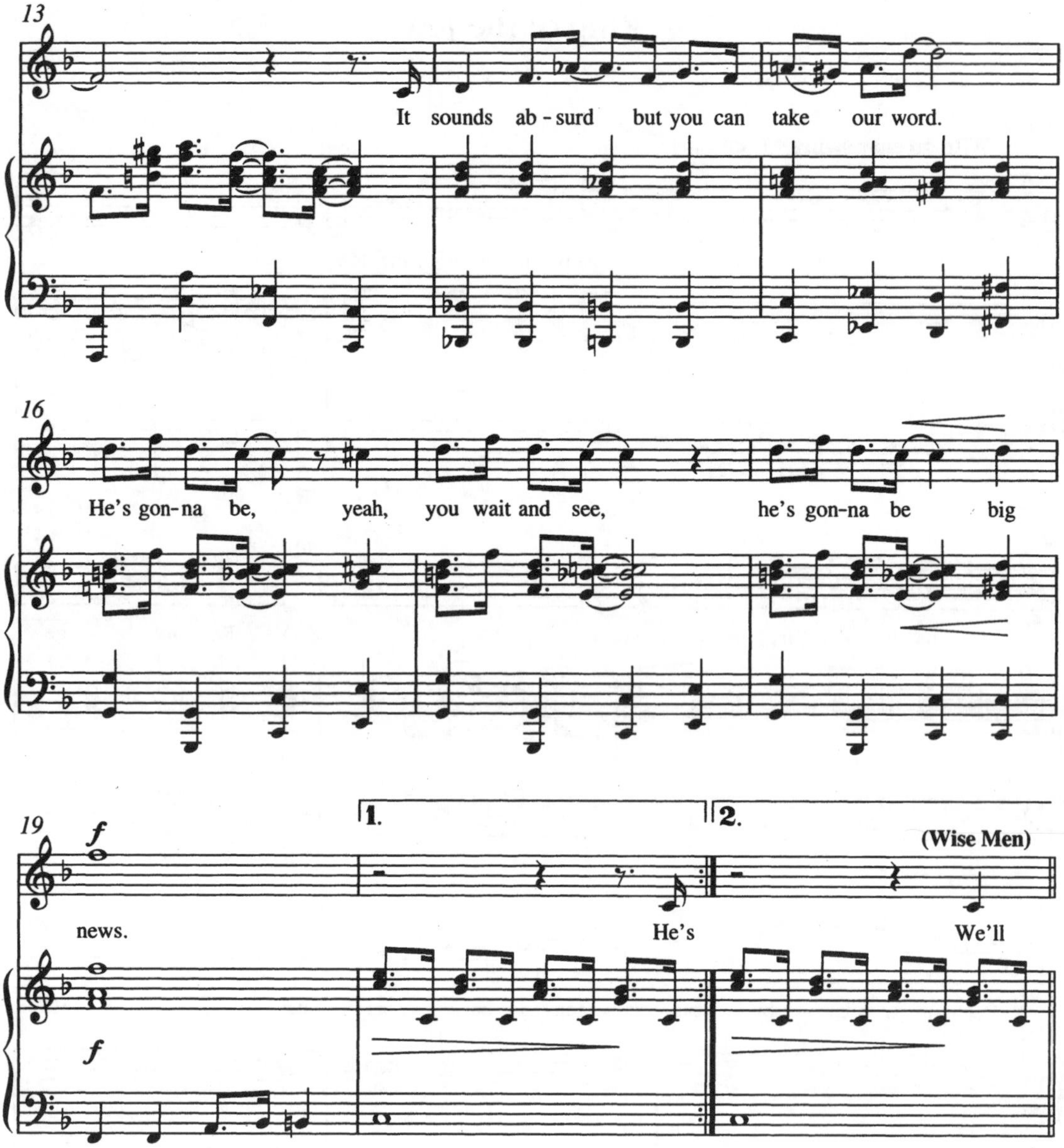
13
It sounds ab - surd but you can take our word.
16
He's gon-na be, yeah, you wait and see, he's gon-na be big
19
f
news.
1.
He's
2.
(Wise Men)
We'll
f

8. Follow that star

22
mf
go, fol-low that star, shin-ing, shin-ing bright. We'll
mf

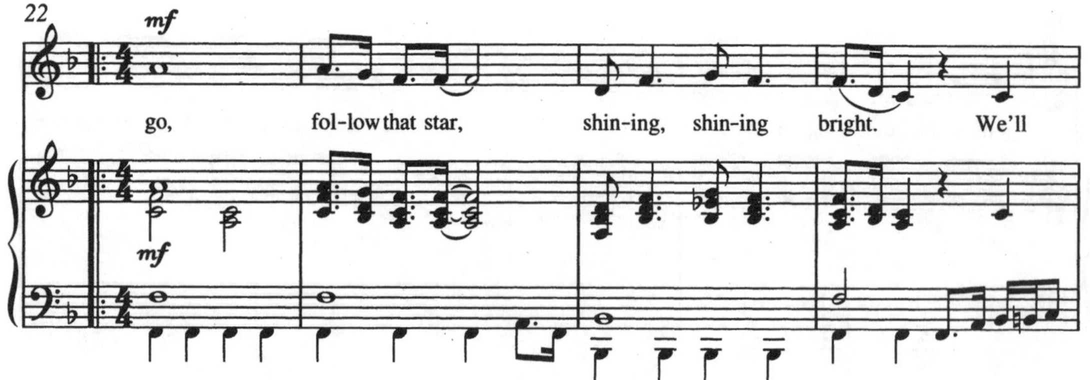

26
go, fol-low that star, shin-ing in the night. We'll
30
get on our ca - mels and, keep-ing our eyes fixed on the star in the
33
skies, we'll ride to the place where it stops and we'll see,
36
that's where the ba - by will be. We'll go,

40
fol-low that star, shin-ing, shin-ing bright. We'll go,
44
1.
(Full Choir)
fol - low that star, shin - ing in the night. We'll
48
2.
(Wise Men) f
Go, fol - low that star.
(Full Choir) f
He's gon - na be the King of the Jews. He's
f
51
Go, fol - low that star, shin - ing,
gon - na be the King of the Jews. O – K, may - be he's

54
shin - ing bright.
on - ly a ba - by, but he's gon - na be big news. He's

57
Go, fol - low that star. Go,
gon - na be the King of the Jews. He's gon - na be the King of the Jews.

60
fol - low that star, shin - ing in the
It sounds ab - surd but you can take our word,

63
night.
he's gon - na be, yeah, you wait and see,
65
rit.
ff
Fol - low that star. Fol - low that star.
he's gon-na be big news.
rit.
ff

Narrator Follow that star . . . It's an unlikely story when you think about it. A baby born to a virgin; well that's a miracle for a start! Lying in a load of straw instead of in a decent cot; visited by poor shepherds and rich magi – all in a stable together, surrounded by smelly animals. Is this the way you would expect the King of the earth to put in his first appearance?

And as you can see, it was all quite a responsibility for me. I mean, if I had gone and got the wrong stable, heaven knows *what* would have happened!

Follow that star. It's an unlikely story when you think about it, but maybe . . . maybe you should.

Do not be afraid (Reprise)

Solo angel

Do not be afraid of the song I sing.
Do not be afraid of the news I bring.
For today you'll see a baby who will be
the greatest king in history.

Angel choir

Do not be afraid of the song we sing.
Do not be afraid of the news we bring.
For today you'll see a baby who will be
the greatest king in history.

Full choir

Glory to God in the highest heaven.
Glory to God in the highest heaven.
And peace to men on earth,
and peace to men on earth.
And peace to men on earth,
and peace to men on earth.

Repeat

Last time: Glory to God.

9. Do not be afraid

13
song we sing.
Do not be a-fraid of the news we bring.
16
For to-day you'll see a ba-by who will be the great-est king in
19
(Full Choir)
ff
his-to-ry.
Glo - ry to God in the
ff
22
high - est heav - ven.
Glo - ry to

25
God in the high - est hea - ven. And peace to men on
f
f
29
earth and peace to men on earth. And peace to men on
33
1.
2.
earth and peace to men on earth. peace to men on
37
rit.
ff
earth. Glo - ry to God.
rit.
ff
8

Please photocopy this page

KEVIN MAYHEW PERFORMANCE AND PHOTOCOPYING LICENCE FORM

We are delighted that you are considering ***Follow that Star*** for production.
Please note that a performance licence is required and royalties are payable as follows:

10% of gross takings, plus VAT
***(Minimum fee: £21.28 + VAT = £25.00)**

This fee is valid until 31 December 2008. After that date, please contact the Copyright Department for information.

This form should be returned to the Copyright Department at Kevin Mayhew Ltd. A copy, including our performance licence number, will be returned to you.

Name of organisation ______________________________

Contact name ______________________________

Contact address ______________________________

____

Postcode ______________________________

Contact telephone no. ______________ **Contact fax no.** ______________

Email ______________________________

Date(s) of performance(s) ______________________________

Venue ______________________________

Seating capacity ______________________________

***Proposed ticket price** ______________________________

Please tick:

☐ I am not charging admission for my performance.
I enclose the minimum fee.

☐ I am charging admission and undertake to submit performance fees due to Kevin Mayhew Ltd. within 28 days of the last performance, together with a statement of gross takings.

☐ I require a words-only photocopying licence and enclose £10.00 (inc. VAT).

Signature ______________________________

Name (please print) ______________________________

On behalf of ______________________________

Address if different from above ______________________________

To be completed by Kevin Mayhew Copyright Department:

Performance/Photocopying Licence No. ______________________________

is issued to ______________ for ______________ performance(s)

of ______________ on ______________

Signed ______________ for Kevin Mayhew Ltd. Date ______________

Copyright Department, Kevin Mayhew Ltd, Buxhall, Stowmarket, Suffolk, IP14 3BW
Telephone number: UK 01449 737978 International +44 1449 737978
Fax number: UK 01449 737834 International +44 1449 737834
Email: copyright@kevinmayhewltd.com